Department of Special Education
ROCHESTER PUBLIC SCHOOLS
Coffman Building
Rochester, Minnesota

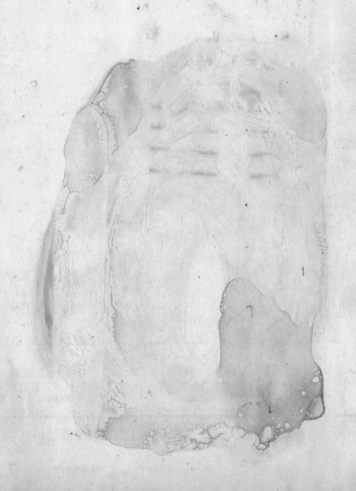

Our
New Friends

by WILLIAM S. GRAY

and MAY HILL ARBUTHNOT

Illustrated by Keith Ward

BASIC READERS : CURRICULUM FOUNDATION SERIES

A Revision of the Elson-Gray Basic Readers

Scott, Foresman and Company

CHICAGO ATLANTA DALLAS NEW YORK

STORIES

New Friends

Our Friends at Work

Our Animal Friends

Our Friends at Play

Story Book Friends

New Friends

The New Family

"Oh, Dick," said Jane.

"No one lives in the new house.

Who will come to live in it?"

From the June, 1938, issue of *The Instructor*. Used by permission of the F. A. Owen Publishing Company. Adapted from "Ann Jean's Neighbor."

Dick said, "It is a big house.
Maybe a big family will live in it."

"Yes," said Jane. "A big, big family.
Maybe the family will have girls.
I want girls to play with."

"Oh, no," said Dick.
"I want boys to play with.
I want boys to live there.
Maybe the family will have boys."

One day Jane said, "Look, look!
A new family will live there soon.
See the dolls and the doll house!
Girls will live in the new house.
I will have girls to play with."

Dick said, "I see a toy horse.
Boys play with toy horses.
Boys will live in the new house.
I will have boys to play with."

That day a blue car came
to the new house.

Dick and Jane saw it.

"There is the family!" said Jane.

"Our new friends have come."

Dick said, "The father is here.

The mother is here, too.

But where are the boys, and
where are the girls?"

Soon a black car came.

"Look, look," said Jane.

"Here comes a grandfather.

Here comes a grandmother.

I see a boy and a girl, too.

We must go and say hello.

Oh, Dick!

The boy looks like the girl.

The girl looks like the boy."

Dick and Jane ran to the car.
They said, "We are Dick and Jane.
Maybe we can help you."

The grandmother said, "Thank you.
This is Peter.
And this is Ellen."

Spot ran to Peter and Ellen.
"Bow-wow, bow-wow," he said.
Jane said, "This is our dog, Spot.
He wants to say hello.
He wants to say hello
to our new friends."

Who Will Ride?

One day Peter ran to Grandmother.
"See my new wagon," he said.
"I will let you ride in it."

"I am too big," said Grandmother.
"I can not ride in the new wagon."

Peter said, "Who will ride with me?
I will run and find Ellen.
Maybe she will ride in my wagon."

12

Peter said, "Come, Ellen.
We can play with my new wagon.
I will let you ride in it.
It can go fast."

Ellen said, "Thank you, Peter.
I can not ride now.
I have work to do.
Run and find our new friends.
Run and find Dick and Jane.
Maybe they will ride with you."

Peter ran out to find Jane.

He said, "Oh, Jane, come and ride.

Come and ride in my new wagon.

Hop in, and we will go fast."

Jane said, "I can not ride now.

I want to make something

for my dolls.

Go and find Dick.

Maybe he will ride with you."

14

Peter saw Dick and said,
"Hello, Dick.

Hop into my new wagon, and
we will have a fast ride."

But Dick said, "No, thank you.
I can not ride now.
I must put a new tail
on this toy cat.
Sally likes to ride.
Let her ride with you."

Sally said, "Yes, Peter, I will ride.
My toys will ride with us."
She put Tim into the wagon.
She put her toy dog into it.
She put her dolls into it, too.
"Oh, Sally!" said Peter.
"All the toys are in the wagon.
Now we can not get in it."
"No," said Sally.
"We will have to walk."
And they did.

Fun in the New House

Down, down came the rain.

"Please, Mother," said Dick.

"We want to walk in the rain.

This is a good day to go and see
Peter and Ellen.

They are the friends who came
to live in the new white house.

Will you please let us go?"

Mother said, "Run and get
the big black umbrella.

You can walk under it."

Splash, splash went the children
under the big umbrella.

It was fun to walk in the rain.

Jane said, "I am a duck.

I can splash like a duck.

I can talk like a duck.

I can say quack, quack."

And away she went
with a quack, quack, quack
and a splash, splash, splash.

Peter saw Dick and Jane come
up the walk under the big umbrella.
He laughed and said, "Hello!
This is a good day to come.
Mother will make cookies soon.
Maybe she will let us help her.
Maybe she will let us make
animal cookies."

"Oh!" said Dick.
"We like to make animal cookies."

Mother let the children make
animal cookies.

Cookie horses and cows.

Cookie dogs and cats.

Cookie rabbits and chickens.

And little cookie ducks.

The children ate the good cookies.

They ate the cookie horses,
and they ate the cookie cows.

They ate the cookie rabbits,
and they ate the cookie cats.

They ate the cookie dogs
and the chickens and the ducks.

Soon it was time to go home.
"Good-by," said Peter and Ellen.
"Good-by," said Dick and Jane.
"It was fun to make cookies.
Now we will have fun in the rain."

Dick went out and put up
the big black umbrella.
"Look up, Dick," laughed Jane.
Dick looked up and said,
"Well, well! Here is the umbrella.
But where is the rain?"

The First Day at School

Peter was happy, and Ellen
was happy, too.

It was the first day at school.

"Oh, my!" said Ellen.

"It is fun to come to school.

It is fun to work and play
with all the boys and girls.

I like school, and I like
all my new friends."

Ellen looked up and saw
the children going out.

"Oh, my!" she said.

"All the boys and girls
are going out.

Maybe it is time to go home.

I will go home, too."

So little Ellen went out
with all the children.

Susan saw Ellen going away.

She saw her going down the walk.

So she said, "Hello, little girl.

My name is Susan.

What is your name?

And where are you going?"

Ellen said, "My name is Ellen.

And I am going home.

It is time for us to go home."

"Oh, no, Ellen," laughed Susan.

"It is not time to go home.

It is time to play with your friends."

A Play House at School

One day Tom wanted to make
a play house.

Peter wanted to help make it.

So did two little girls.

"Let us make a big play house,"
said Peter.

"We can have fun in it.

We can put all our toys in it."

"Yes, yes," said the children.

"Let us make a big play house."

Soon there was a big play house.

In went the girls and the boys.

In went the dolls and the toys.

"Now we can play," said Tom.

"Oh, Tom," said Peter.

"Let us find Ellen first.

She will want to play with us."

The children went to get Ellen.

But they did not find her.

So they went into the house

to play with all the toys.

"Oh, here is Ellen!" said Peter.
"She was here all the time.
See what she did to our house!"

"Oh, my!" said Ellen.
"I did not know this was
your play house.

I wanted to make a boat.

Now I must take my boat and
help you make your house."

The Big Umbrella

Mother said, "See it rain.
This is a good day to take
your new umbrella to school."

Jane said, "Please let me take
the big black umbrella.

I like to walk under it."

Mother said, "The black umbrella
is too big for a little girl.
But I know you like it.
So I will let you take it."

Splash, splash came the rain.

Down on the street.

Down on the walk.

And down on the black umbrella.

A boy was going down the walk.

So was a little girl.

But Jane did not see them.

And they did not see Jane.

Bump! Bump!

"Oh!" said Jane. "Who is that?"

The boy laughed and said,
"My name is Jim."

And the girl said, "My name
is Patty.

See that big yellow house
down the street.

That is our new home.

We are going to school now.

This is our first day at your school."

Jane said, "My name is Jane.

I am going to school, too.

I will walk to school with you."

Then the rain came down fast.
Splash, splash, splash, splash!
Jane saw it splash on Patty.
She saw it splash on Jim.
So she said to them, "Oh, my!
Where is your umbrella?"

"We lost it," said Patty.
"And we can not find it."
Then Jane said, "I will take you
to school under my umbrella.
This umbrella is too big for me.
But it is not too big for three."

The Lost Pennies

"Oh, Jane," said Patty.

"I can not go home in the rain.

So I am going to eat at school.

I have pennies to buy something.

But I do not know what to buy.

Will you please help me?"

"Yes, Patty," said Jane.

"Susan and I are going to eat
at school, too.

We will all get something good."

First Jane saw something red.
"Look at that," she said.
"That looks good.
I am going to buy that."

"So am I," said Susan.
"So am I," said Patty.
"I know I will like it, too.
That is what I will buy."

Soon Jane said, "I have all I want."

"So have I," said Patty.

Then she looked in her pocket.

"Oh, Susan!" she said.

"I have lost my pennies.

Maybe I lost them on the street."

Then Patty saw Jim come in.

She said, "Oh, Jim, my pennies
are not in my pocket.

I have lost them.

Now I can not eat at school."

Jim laughed and said,
"I know where your pennies are.
They are not in your pocket.
But they are not lost.
You did not put your pennies
in your pocket.
You did not take them to school.
I saw them at home, and
I put them in my pocket.
Here they are!
Now you can buy something to eat!"

A Big Friend

"Come, Puff," said Sally.

"I want to go for a walk.

We will walk and walk."

Away went Sally, and away went
her yellow kitten.

They walked, and they walked,
and they walked.

At last Sally said, "Oh, Puff!
It is time to go home."
Sally looked up the street.
Then she looked down the street.
"Where is our house?" she said.
"Oh, my! We are lost!
I do not know the way home."

Sally sat down.
Puff sat down with her.
They sat and sat and sat.

At last Sally saw a man.

She said, "Hello, big man.

My kitten and I went for a walk.

We walked and walked.

Now we want to go home.

But we are lost.

We do not know the way home.

We do not know which way to go."

"Well, well," said the big man.

"Maybe I can help you.

Where do you live, little girl?"

Sally said, "I live at home.

But I do not know where it is."

The man said, "Do you know

your name, little girl?"

"Oh, yes," she said. "I know it.

My name is Sally."

The man said, "You have two names.

Sally is your first name.

What is your last name?"

But Sally said, "My name is Sally.

My first name is Sally, and

my last name is Sally.

What is your name?"

"I am Big Bill," said the man.

"I am your friend.

I like to help girls and boys.

I will help you find your home."

"Mew, mew," said Puff.

Then she walked away.

Big Bill looked at her.

He said, "Look, Sally Sally.

Maybe your kitten is going home.

Maybe she knows which way to go.

Come, Sally Sally.

Let us go with her."

So away they went.

Puff and Big Bill and Sally.

At last Puff saw a white house.

She saw Mother and Jane and
Dick and Spot.

"Mew, mew," she said.

"Bow-wow, bow-wow," said Spot.

Mother ran to Sally and Big Bill.

"Oh, thank you!" she said.

"You have found our baby.

You found our Sally."

Sally said, "Oh, no, I found Big Bill.
I found a new friend."

Patty and Her Pennies

One day Patty said, "My pennies
are in my blue pig.

I will take out five pennies.

I want to buy something for Mother.

Something for her birthday."

Bump, bump, bump!

Out came three pennies.

Bump, bump, out came two pennies.

"Here are five pennies," said Patty.

"One, two, three, four, five!"

Then she ran to the store.

Patty saw something she wanted
in the store.

She said, "This one is pretty.

It is blue and yellow.

The red and white one is pretty, too.

Which one do I want?

Which one will Mother like
for her birthday?

Let me see. Let me see.

Maybe Mother will like
the red and white one.

That is the one I will take."

Patty looked in her pocket
for her five pennies.

"Oh, my! Oh, my!" she said.

"I can not find my pennies.

I put them in my pocket.

Maybe I lost them on the way
to the store.

I must go and look for them."

So Patty ran out to look
for her five pennies.

Patty saw Big Bill on the street.
"Hello," she said.
"I have lost my five pennies."
Big Bill said, "Well, well.
Look in your pocket."

"I looked in my pocket," said Patty.
Big Bill said, "You have two pockets.
Which pocket did you look in?"
"In my big pocket," said Patty.
"Well," said Big Bill.
"Now look in your little pocket.
Maybe your pennies are there."

"Yes, here they are!" said Patty.
"I have found them at last.
I found them in my little pocket.
Here are all my pennies.
One, two, three, four, five!"

Big Bill laughed and laughed.
Patty laughed, too.
"Thank you, Big Bill," she said.
"Now I will take my pennies
to the store.
Now I can get something pretty
for Mother.
Something for her birthday!"

Our Friends at Work

Time to Work

"Oh, look!" said Father.

"See what time it is.

It is time for me to go to work.

I must hurry."

So Father said good-by
to all the family.

And away he went to work.

"Come, Dick," said Jane.
"It is time to help Mother.
We must hurry and take things
out to her."

In and out went Dick and Jane.
In and out! In and out!
At last Dick said, "Come, Jane.
This is all we can do now.
It is time for us to go to school."
So away ran Dick and Jane.

"Look! Look!" said Mother.

"It is time for me to go
to the store.

My family must have
something good to eat.

I must buy things for dinner.

I must hurry and buy things
for dinner."

Sally said, "Oh, Mother!
It is time for me to work.
Please let me do something, too."

Mother said, "Here, Sally.
Here is the basket.
You can go to the store with me.
You can take the basket and
get something for dinner."

Little Sally was happy.
She said, "I can work, too.
It is time for me to work now.
I can take the basket to the store
for Mother."

Who Will Help Tom?

"Oh, my!" said Tom one day.
"Look at all the things in here.
One old black umbrella,

one old basket,

two toy dogs,

a toy cat,

a red ball,

a little toy pig,

and Tim!"

"Hello, Tom," said Peter.

"Come and play with my wagon."

Tom said, "Oh, I am too busy.

Look at all the things in here.

I must take them all out and

put them away.

I have found your red ball.

Will you please take it home?"

"Not now," said Peter.

"I want to ride in my wagon first.

I will take it home after dinner."

And away walked Peter.

After Peter went away, Patty came.

"Hello, Patty," said Tom.

"I have found your basket.

Will you please take it home?"

"I am too busy," said Patty.

"I must take my dolls for a ride.

After I come back, I will help you.

I will take my basket then."

So away went Patty with her dolls.

Dick saw Tom at work.

He said, "Come with me, Tom.

Jack wants us to come and play

with his new ball."

"Thank you, Dick," said Tom.

"I am too busy to play now.

I have found the things

that you and Sally lost.

I have found your old umbrella, and

I have found Tim.

Will you take them home?"

"Not now," said Dick.

"I am going to play ball.

After I play ball with Jack,

I will come back and help you."

Then away went Dick in a hurry.

All at once Tom looked up and
saw his four friends.

Patty and Peter were back.

And so were Jack and Dick.

"Hello, Tom," said Dick.

"We all came back.

We came back to help you.

We can all do the work
in a hurry.

After that we can play."

Sally Helps

Dick and Jane and Mother and
Sally were on the way to the farm.
Jim and Patty were with them.
They were going to eat dinner
with Grandfather and Grandmother.

"Oh, Dick," said Patty.
"Will we come to the farm soon?"
"Pretty soon," said Dick.
"Look for a farm that has
a big white barn and a yellow house.
That is where Grandmother lives."

Soon they came to a big farm.
"This is the farm," said Mother.
"This is where Grandfather lives."

All at once Dick said, "Oh, look!
Grandfather has a new house.
He has a new white house."

"No, no," laughed Mother.
"This is not a new house.
This is the old house.
Once its color was yellow.
But now it has white paint on it."

The children ran to the barn.
Grandfather was busy there.
"Oh, Grandfather," said Dick.
"Your house has a new color.
Did you paint it white?"

"Yes, I did," said Grandfather.
"And now I am going to paint
the barn a new color.
I am going to paint it red."
Dick said, "Please, Grandfather!
Let us help you paint the barn."

Grandfather said, "Boys and girls are too little to paint barns.

But you can paint the hen house.

You can paint it white."

So Grandfather painted his barn.

Dick and Jane and Patty and Jim painted the hen house.

They painted and painted.

They painted fast.

Swish went the paint.

Swish! Swish!

Swish, swish, swish!

Sally was busy in the hen house.
Soon she came out and said,
"I painted something, too!
Guess what I painted."
The four children ran and looked.
"Oh, Sally!" they said.
"You have painted the eggs!"

"Yes," said Sally.
"I made the eggs a pretty color.
I made them a very pretty color.
Now the hens have pretty eggs."

"Cluck, cluck!" said the hens.

Old Toy Horse

Toy Horse was very, very old.

One day Peter said, "Look, Ellen.

Look at our old toy horse.

Look at his head.

Look at his feet.

Look at his funny tail.

Once he was pretty.

But now he is very old.

Now he is too old to play with."

Next day Father went to a store.

He came back with a new toy horse.

The new horse was black and white.

His head was white.

His tail was white.

His feet were black.

And black spots were on his back.

Peter said, "We must have a name
for our new toy horse.

What can we name him?

He looks like Old Toy Horse.

Let us name him New Toy Horse."

Ellen said, "What can we do
with Old Toy Horse?"

"We can give him away," said Peter.

"We can give him to Billy."

"Billy will not want him,"
said Ellen.

"No one will want him.

Old Toy Horse is not very pretty.

But we can make him pretty.

We can make a new tail for him.

We can make two new feet for him.

We can put his head on.

We can paint him white, and
we can paint black spots on him.

After we have painted him,
we will give him away.

Then Billy will like him."

After dinner all the family
worked on Old Toy Horse.

They worked and worked.

They put his head on.

They made a new tail for him.

They made two new feet for him.

Next they painted him white and
painted black spots on his back.

Then they painted his feet black.

"Now look at Old Toy Horse,"
said Peter.

"He looks like New Toy Horse."

"Well, well," said Father.

"We have made Old Toy Horse
look like New Toy Horse.

I don't know which is which.

I don't know which horse
you want to give to Billy."

All at once Peter and Ellen ran
to Old Toy Horse.

They said, "This is Old Toy Horse.

We don't want to give him away.

Let us give the new horse to Billy."

And that is what they did.

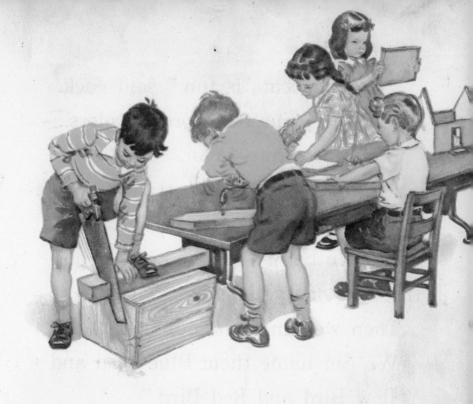

Making Boats

S-s-s! S-s-s went the saws.

The children were very busy.

They were busy making things
at school.

The girls were making a doll house.

The boys were making boats.

"Making boats is fun," said Jack.

"Let us paint them pretty colors.

Blue is a pretty color.

Red and yellow are pretty colors, too.

We can paint one boat blue.

We can paint the next one red and
the next one yellow.

Then we can name our boats.

We can name them Blue Bird and
Yellow Bird and Red Bird."

The boys worked fast, and soon
all the boats were made.

Next day the boys went to play
with the boats.

"Go, Red Bird, go!" said Dick.

"Go, Yellow Bird!" said Jack.

"Go, Blue Bird!" said Billy.

Away went the boats.

They went very fast.

"See them go!" said Billy.

"Which one will get there first?"

The boys ran to get the boats.
"Here is Blue Bird," said Billy.
"It went very, very fast.
And it came in first."

"Here comes Red Bird," said Jack.
"It will come in next.
But I don't see Yellow Bird.
The yellow boat is lost.
I can't guess where it went."

All at once Dick said, "Look!
I have found the yellow boat.
And there is a funny animal on it.
It is going to walk away.
But it can't walk fast.
It is a poky little animal.
Let us take it to school and
name it Poky."

Billy said, "Hurry and see Poky.
His head and feet are going
into the house on his back.
What a funny animal Poky is!
His house is on his back."

The Little House

Splash! Splash came the rain.

"Oh, my," said Jim.

"I can't go outdoors to play.

What can I do in the house?"

His father said, "Don't you want

to help me make a house?

I am making a house for a family."

"A house for a family!" said Jim.

"We can't make one as big as that."

But Father said, "You will see."

S-s-s! S-s-s! S-s-s! S-s-s!

Bang! Bang! Bang!

Father worked, and Jim worked.

After a time Jim said, "The house we are making is very little.

It is too little for a family.

A family can't live in a house as little as this one."

"Oh, yes," said Father.

"I know a family that can live in this house."

All at once Jim said, "I can guess who will live in this house.

A doll family will live in it!

It is a doll house for Patty."

But Father said, "You will see."

Bang! Bang! Bang!

At last Father said, "Now we can stop our work.

The house is made."

"Oh," said Jim. "Now I see.

We have made a house for a bird family."

"Now we will paint the house
a pretty color," said Father.
"We will paint it green."
So they painted the house green.
Then Jim wanted to go outdoors
and put the house up in a tree.
"We can't go out now," said Father.
"But we will go as soon as
the rain stops."

And soon the rain did stop.
So Father and Jim went outdoors.
They put the little green house
up in a tree.

Soon Jim and his father saw
two blue birds come to the tree.

The birds sat in the tree and
looked at the little green house.

Then they went away.

"Oh, Father!" said Jim.

"The birds don't like our house."

But all at once he saw the birds
come back to the tree.

"Look!" said Jim.

"The blue birds are going to live
in our little green house.

They like the little house
we made for them."

Patty Reads to Baby

"Oh, Patty," said Mother one day.

"I am very busy, and Baby
will not go to sleep.

Will you stop your play and
read to him?"

"Yes, Mother," said Patty.

"I will stop and read to Baby.

I will give him his toy dog and
read to him.

Maybe he will go to sleep then."

Patty said, "Look, Baby.
See this pretty book.
I will read a good story to you.
Then you will go to sleep."

Baby looked at the story book.
He did not want to go to sleep.
He wanted to talk and talk.
"Pretty, pretty book," he said.
"Read! Read! Read a story!
Read to Baby."

Patty sat down to read a story.

She said, "I will read fast, and
Baby will soon go to sleep.

Then I can go outdoors and
play with Susan."

So she began to read very fast.

But Baby did not go to sleep.
He began to jump up and down.
He began to laugh and talk.
"Funny, funny!" he said.
"Funny, funny story!
Pretty, pretty book!"

Patty said, "Oh, Baby, don't talk.
It is time to go to sleep.
Please hurry and go to sleep."
Patty began to read slower.
Baby did not laugh and talk.
He did not jump up and down.
But he did not go to sleep.

Then Patty began to read slower
and slower and slower.
At last Mother came in.
Baby said, "See Patty!
Patty went to sleep!"

Our Animal Friends

Happy Finds a Friend

One day Billy was going to school.
When he came to the pet store,
he walked slower.
"I have time to stop," he said.
"So I will look at the animals."
He saw some yellow chickens,
some white rabbits, and some kittens.
He saw some birds, too.
Red, green, and all colors!
Then Billy saw a little black dog.
It looked and looked at Billy.

The man in the store could see
Billy and the black dog.

When the man came out, Billy said,
"That black dog is not happy.

He wants to run and jump.

He wants to play outdoors.

He wants a home.

He looks like a dog in my book.

I wish I could have him.

I wish I could give him a home."

After school Billy went back
to the pet store.

When the black dog saw Billy,
he began to jump up and down.

He made Billy laugh.

Billy said, "You funny little dog!
I wish I could buy you.
Maybe Father will buy you for me.
I will ask him.
Good-by, little dog."

As soon as Billy was home,
he ran to find his mother.

"Oh, Mother!" he said.

"Guess what I saw in the pet store.
I saw a little black dog.
I wish I could have him.
I will ask Father to buy him."

At last Billy saw his father
coming home to dinner.

"Oh, Father!" said Billy.

"I want to ask you something.
Will you buy a dog for me?
I saw a little dog in the pet store.
I wish he could be my dog.
Please buy him for me."

Father said, "A birthday is coming.
A birthday is coming soon.
Maybe you will get your wish
when your birthday comes."

Soon the birthday came.

"Happy birthday!" said Nancy.

"Happy birthday!" said Mother.

"Happy birthday!" said Father.

"See all your things," said Nancy.

"A book and a ball and a car!"

Then Billy saw a big basket.

"Look in the basket," said Nancy.

"Guess what is in it."

All at once a dog said, "Bow-wow."

When Billy saw the black dog,
he began to laugh and laugh.

"Oh, oh!" he said.

"Thank you, Father, thank you.
This is the dog I wanted!"

Nancy said, "He looks very happy.
Let's name him Happy."

"Yes, Nancy," said Billy.

"I think that will be a good name
for this dog.

He looks happy, and he is happy.

So let's name him Happy."

Puff Has a Ride

Dick wanted to give Puff some milk.

He called and called her.

He looked in the house, and
he looked outdoors.

But he could not find the kitten.

"Oh, Jane," called Dick.

"Where can Puff be?

I wish I could find her.

Do you think she has run away?"

Jane said, "A man is coming
with things from the store.
Maybe he saw Puff on the street.
Maybe he saw which way she went.
Let's ask him."

"Hello," called Dick. "Our kitten
has run away from home.
Did you see our yellow kitten?"
"No," said the man.
"I did not see it.
But I will look for your kitten
on my way back to the store."

Big Bill was coming up the street.
Jane said, "Maybe he saw Puff.
Let's ask him."
So Dick called, "Hello, Big Bill.
Did you see our yellow kitten?"

Big Bill said, "No, Dick.
I did not see your kitten, and
I don't know where she could be.
I see the milk wagon coming.
Maybe the milk man saw Puff.
Let's ask him when he stops."

Slower and slower and slower
came the milk wagon.

The milk man was in it, and
next to him sat a yellow kitten.

Big Bill began to laugh.

The milk man laughed, too.

"Here is your kitten," he said.

"I found her in my wagon
when I came out of a house.

I think she wanted to get
some milk from my wagon.

I think she is a funny kitten."

A Friend Comes to School

All the children in the school room
were very busy.

Some of them had paints.

Some of them had story books.

Billy had some paints, and
he was making some green trees.

Jim had a good story book, and
he began to read.

Susan wanted to read, too.

So she found a story book and
began to read it.

Jack was making a farm, and
Dick was making a barn on it.

All at once a little black dog
came to the door of the school room.

Jack saw it and began to laugh.

"Oh, Billy," he called.

"Guess who has come to school.
I think he wants to see you."

Then Billy looked up and saw
the little black dog at the door.

It was Happy.

When Happy saw Billy, he jumped up and down.

He began to run, and he bumped into all the things in the room.

He bumped into the play house.

Bang! Bang! Down it came!

He bumped into the farm.

Bang! Bang! Down came the barn!

He bumped into the paints.

Then he jumped on Billy.

He was as happy as he could be.

Happy was so funny that he made the children laugh.

But Billy did not laugh.

He said, "Oh, Happy!

You bumped into all our things.

Look at the paints!

Look at the farm!

Look at the barn!

You must go away from here.

You want to play all the time.

I am too busy to play with you.

Go home, Happy, go home."

Happy went out of the room and out into the school yard.

But he did not go home.

He sat down in the yard.

When Billy came out of school, Happy was at the door.

He ran to Billy and jumped on him.

Billy said, "Come, Happy.

Let's go home.

School is not for dogs.

School is for children who work."

Poky Gets Lost

One day Nancy went to feed Poky.

"Oh, look at Poky!" she called.

"His head is out.

His head is out of his house."

All the children came to see the pet.

"Hello, Poky," they said.

But Poky did not say hello to them.

Back into his house went his head.

"Poky wants to sleep," said Nancy.

"He sleeps all day and all night."

It was time for the children
to go home from school.

But Nancy did not go with them.

It was her time to feed the pets.

Every pet had to have its dinner.

First she ran to feed the rabbits.

Then she went to feed the chickens
and the little yellow bird.

At last she came to Poky.

"Oh, Poky," she said. "Now I
will get something for you."

Away she ran to get his dinner.

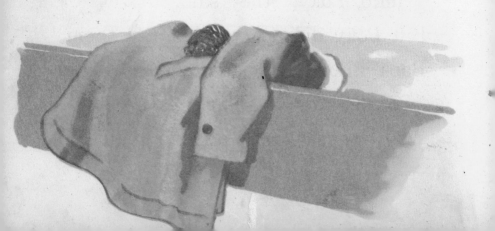

But when Nancy came back
to feed Poky, he was not there.

"Poky, Poky!" she called.

She looked under every thing
in the room.

She looked back of every door.

But she could not find Poky.

"Oh, my!" she said. "I wish
I could find our dear little pet.

It will soon be night, and Mother
will look for me."

So Nancy had to hurry home.

"Mother! Mother!" said Nancy.
"When I went to feed Poky,
I could not find him.
I looked for him everywhere."
Mother said, "I don't think Poky
walked out of the school room.
I think he will be there when
you go back in the morning."

All at once Nancy said, "O-oh!
There is something in my pocket!
It jumped and jumped.
Oh! I have found dear Poky!
He was in my pocket all the time!"

Bunny Boy

Dick and Jane had a white rabbit.

His name was Bunny Boy.

He had a house to live in, but he
wanted to play in the yard.

One morning Bunny Boy found
a way to get the door open.

Hop, hop, hop! Away he ran.

He looked for Dick and Jane.

He looked for Spot and Puff.

He looked everywhere in the yard.

Hop, hop, hop went Bunny Boy.

Soon Bunny Boy came
to a little door.

It was open, and so he jumped in.

What a surprise Bunny had!

Down he fell with a big bump.

He fell into a room under the house.

He fell on something black.

Something as black as night!

Then Bunny wanted to get out.

He jumped and jumped. But he
could not jump up to the little door.

So he sat there all day.

Night was coming, and Dick went
to feed the pets.

When he came to the rabbit house,
he saw the open door.

"Where is Bunny?" said Dick.

"He was here this morning."

Sally and Jane helped Dick
look for Bunny Boy.

Mother and Father helped, too.

They looked everywhere, but they
could not find the dear little rabbit.

At last night came, and they
had to go in and eat dinner.

But Dick and Jane could not eat.

They sat and thought of Bunny.

They thought and thought.

Where, oh, where could Bunny be?

All at once Spot and Puff ran
to a door in the next room.

"Bow-wow, bow-wow," said Spot.

"Mew, mew," said Puff.

Just then something bumped
on the door.

It bumped and bumped.

Every one ran to the door.

Then there was another bump and
another and another.

"Let's open the door," said Father.

"Yes, let's open it," said Dick.

"Let's see what is there."

What a surprise they had!

What a big surprise!

"Here is a rabbit!" said Jane.

"But it is not Bunny Boy.

This rabbit is black.

It must be another rabbit.

Where did it come from?

How did it get here?"

Just then Puff ran to the rabbit.

"Mew, mew," she said.

"Look at Puff," laughed Dick.
"She is making the rabbit white.
Oh! This is Bunny Boy!
Well, well! What a surprise!
We did not know our pet.
We thought he was another rabbit.
We thought he was black.
But Puff made him white."

"Dear, dear Bunny!" said Jane.
"How did you get so black?"
Dick's father said, "I can guess."
Dick said, "I can guess, too."

Who Took the Nuts?

One morning Dick and Jane had
a good surprise at the farm.

"Oh, look!" said Dick. "The nuts
fell from the trees last night.

They fell everywhere in the yard.

Let's get every one of them."

So Dick took a basket and
began to put nuts into it.

Jane helped him, and soon
every nut was in Dick's basket.

Just then Grandfather called Dick.
Dick put the basket under a tree.
Then he ran to the barn and
helped Grandfather feed the cows.
Jane ran into the house and
helped Grandmother get dinner.

Soon a little gray animal
looked down from the tree.
What a big gray tail it had!
It was a squirrel.
It looked at the basket, and
it looked at the nuts.
Swish, swish went its tail.
And down the tree it ran.

Gray Squirrel took a nut
from Dick's basket.

Up the tree he ran with it.

Then he ran down and took
another nut.

He took one nut after another.

Up and down! Up and down!

How that busy squirrel worked!

Gray Squirrel worked all day.

But when night came,
he went to sleep in the tree.

Next morning Dick and Jane
went out to get the nuts.

But they did not see any nuts
in Dick's basket.

"Oh, Grandmother!" called Jane.

"Who took all the nuts
from Dick's basket?

Did you eat any of them?

Did Grandfather eat any of them?"

"Oh, no," said Grandmother.

"We did not take any of the nuts."

Just then a nut fell
from the tree.

It fell down and bumped
Dick's head.

How Dick jumped!

He looked up and began to laugh.

"Well, well," he said.

"Now I know who took the nuts."

"Yes," said Grandmother.

"Gray Squirrel lives in that tree.

He has put the nuts away.

When the snow comes,
he will have some food to eat."

The Snow Party

Down, down fell the snow.
It fell everywhere.
It fell all day and all night.
Next morning Susan looked out.
"Oh, Father!" she said.
"How pretty the yard looks!
I want to go outdoors and play
in the snow."

"Well, Susan," said her father.
"Let's go outdoors now.
Let's go out in the yard and
have a snow party."

"A snow party!" said Susan.
"I can't guess what that is.
What is a snow party?"
Father said, "You will see.
And I think you will like it.
First we must get some food.
We must take a basket of food
to a snow party."

Susan found a basket and helped
Father put some food into it.
They put some nuts and cookies
and corn into the basket. They put
some apples into it, too.

Then Father took Susan outdoors.

He took her to the green tree
in the yard.

"We will put all the food
under this tree," he said.

"We will have our party here."

Father put the basket down, and
he began to take out the food.

Susan helped him.

And soon the corn and cookies and
apples and nuts were on the snow.

When Susan took out the corn,
she said, "We can't eat this.

We can eat the cookies and apples
and nuts. But who will eat the corn?"

Father just said, "You will see.

You will have a big surprise."

"I don't see any boys and girls," said Susan.

"But I can guess who is coming to our snow party."

"Yes," said Father. "I thought you could guess who is coming. But we must not let them see us. We must get behind a tree."

So Father and Susan walked away from the green tree.

They went behind another tree.

Soon two little gray birds came.

Another little gray bird came and
behind it another and another.

Next five red birds and
four blue birds came.

The birds began to eat the apples
and the cookies.

Then a squirrel and a rabbit came.

The squirrel ate nuts and corn.

The rabbit ate apples.

Susan could see all the animals
from behind the tree.

She said, "A snow party is fun.

Fun for us and fun for the animals."

Red Hen and the Valentine

"See all the valentines," said Billy.
"My, my! What pretty colors!
There are valentines of every color.
I must buy one for Nancy.
Valentine Day will soon be here."

Billy looked at every valentine
in the store.
At last the man said, "Well, Billy.
Which one do you want to buy?"
Billy said, "I think I will buy
this green and white one."

The man said, "You can buy
any valentine for five pennies.
So take any one you like."
But Billy did not have five pennies.
He had just three pennies
in his pocket.
Billy thought and thought.
At last he said, "I have a pet hen.
She gives me an egg every day.
Will you let me have the valentine
for three pennies and an egg?"

"Yes, Billy," said the man.
"You can buy the valentine
for three pennies and one egg.
Run home and get an egg.
Then come back and get
the green and white valentine."

Billy ran home as fast as he could.

He went to see his pet hen.

"Cluck, cluck," she said.

There was an egg in her nest.

"Thank you, Red Hen!" said Billy.

Then he took the egg and ran

back to the store.

He said to the man, "Here is an egg.

And here are my three pennies."

"Good!" said the man.

"And here is your valentine."

Billy went home and put
the valentine in a book.

He said, "Nancy reads this book
every day.

So I know she will find
my surprise in the morning."

Next day was Valentine Day.
When Nancy began to read
her book, she had two surprises.

One surprise was the valentine.

Another surprise was what she
saw on it. This is what she saw,
"Dear Nancy,
This is from Billy and Red Hen."

A Home in a Tree

Two robins were making a nest
in an old apple tree.

The tree was behind the house.

Every day Patty and Jim could see
the robins at work.

Soon after the nest was made,
the children had a surprise.

They saw some pretty blue eggs
in the nest.

One, two, three, four blue eggs!

All at once Jim saw the birds
fly to the apple tree.

He said, "See the mother robin
and the father robin."

"Yes, I see them," said Patty.

"But which is the mother robin?
And which is the father robin?"

Just then the children saw
one of the birds fly to the nest.

It sat on the four blue eggs.

"Oh!" said Jim. "That must be
the mother robin."

Day after day the mother robin
sat on the eggs. But one morning
Jim had another surprise.

He saw four little heads in the nest.

"Oh, Patty!" he called.

"Four baby robins have come
out of the eggs."

Then the big robins were very busy.

They worked all day to feed
the little robins.

All day they came to the nest
with things to eat.

They worked day after day
to feed the little robins.

Soon one baby robin wanted
to fly from the nest.

But it could not fly.

Down it fell into the yard!

When the big robins saw it,
they called and called to it.

But the little bird could not fly
up to the nest.

So the big robins had to fly down
and feed the little bird.

They could feed it, but they
could not put it back in the nest.

Patty and Jim were in the yard when the baby bird fell.

Patty saw it under the apple tree.

"Look, Jim!" she called.

"A little bird fell from the tree. It can't fly up to its nest."

Jim said, "We must help it. I will put it back in the nest."

So Jim went up the tree and put the little robin back in its nest.

At last the baby robins could fly.

They began to fly here and there
in the yard.

They could find things to eat.

And soon the big robins
did not have to feed them.

After that the robins did not
go back to the nest.

Patty said, "Now the birds
have said good-by to the nest.

They have said good-by
to the home in the tree.

They are too big to live in it."

Our Friends at Play

The Lost Toys

Down and up, down and up
went Jane's green ball.

All at once the ball went
over Jane's head.

"Oh," laughed Jane.

"Did it go over the trees?
Did it go over the house?"

"No," said Nancy. "It went
over your head and fell behind you.
I did not see just where it went."
Nancy helped Jane look for it.
They looked everywhere in the yard.

All at once the girls found
something behind the dog house.

But it was not Jane's green ball.
It was a doll.

"This is a surprise," said Nancy.

"I lost that doll this morning, and
I am very glad to find it.

Now I wish we could find
your ball."

The girls looked in the yard again.
Then they looked in the street.
But they did not find Jane's ball.

Billy saw Jane and Nancy looking
for something. So he helped them.
Soon he called, "Oh, girls!
Here is a toy boat in the dog house.
Were you playing with this boat?
Is this what you are looking for?"
"No, Billy," said Nancy.
"We are looking for Jane's ball."

Jane looked at the boat and said,
"How did Dick's boat get here?
He was looking everywhere
for it last night. He will be glad
to have it again."

Billy looked in the dog house again.
This time he saw something blue.
"Here is Sally's toy car," he said.
"How did Sally's little blue car
get in the dog house?"

"Well, well!" said Nancy.
"I am glad we have found my doll
and Dick's boat and Sally's car.
But I wish we could find Jane's ball."
So the children looked again
for the little green ball.

All at once Billy said, "Oh, girls.
Come and see something funny.
Happy has found Jane's green ball.
He is playing with it."
The girls ran to see Happy.
They were just in time to see
him going into his house.
He had Jane's green ball.
The children began to laugh.
"Well, well!" said Nancy.
"I am glad we saw Happy.
I am glad we know where to find
our things when they are lost."

Playing Store

One day Dick was playing store.

Many toys were in the store, and
the big umbrella was over it.

Ellen and Jane were looking
at all the toys.

"Come to Dick's store," said Jack.

"Come and buy something."

Jane said, "I want a store, too."

Then she ran into the house.

Ellen went with her to find
some things for Jane's store.

Soon the girls came back again.
They had found many things
for Jane's store.

"Now," said Jane. "I can have
a store, too.

Dick has a toy store, but I
will have a food store.

Here are apples and cookies and
eggs and milk. And here are
many other good things.

Many, many other things!

You can all buy food from me."

It was time for Mother
to get dinner for her family.

She was looking for the food.

But she could not find any milk
or any eggs.

She looked for other things, too.

"Where is all the food?"
she thought.

"I have looked everywhere.

But there is nothing to eat.

Nothing at all!

I can't get dinner for my family."

Sally was looking for her toys.
She could not find the cars
or the boats or the dolls or Tim.
She looked everywhere in the room.
She looked under things, and
she looked behind things.
Then she ran to ask Mother
where all the toys were.
"Oh, Mother," she said.
"Who has Tim?
Who has all the other toys?
I can't find any of them."

"Let's look outdoors," said Mother.
So she and Sally walked
out into the yard.

They saw the food in Jane's store.

They saw Sally's toys in Dick's store.

And they saw the umbrella over it.

"Oh!" said Mother. "The children
are playing with our things."

When Dick saw Mother, he called,
"Oh, look! We are playing store.
See how many things we have!"

Mother laughed and said, "I see!
You have many things, but you
did not ask for them.
You did not ask for Sally's toys.
You did not ask for the milk or
the eggs or any of the other things.
Now Sally wants her toys again.
And I must take the food for dinner."

So Mother and Sally took the food.
They took the boats and the cars.
They took the dolls and Tim.
Then there was nothing at all
in Jane's store and nothing at all
in Dick's store.
Not an apple or an egg or a cookie.
Not a car or a boat or a doll.
Nothing at all! Nothing at all!

The Wind and the Umbrella

Oo-oo, oo-oo went the wind.

It began to push the umbrella and helped push the red wagon.

"Oh!" said Jane. "I am glad we have an umbrella over us.

The wind can push the umbrella and make us go fast.

The wind will make the wagon go down the street in a hurry."

Oo-oo went the wind. Oo-oo!

Push! Push! Push! Push!

Away went the wagon.

Away it went with Dick and Jane
and the big black umbrella.

The wagon went very fast.

Faster and faster it went
down the street.

Swish! Swish! Swish! Swish!

Soon Jane said, "Oh, Dick!
It is time to go home.
The wind will push us home."
So Dick stopped the wagon.
"Now," he said. "We will go
the other way.

Now the wind can push us
all the way home."

The wind pushed and pushed.

"Oh, Dick!" said Jane. "Help me!
We must put the umbrella down.
The wind can't push us the way
we want to go.

It can push us one way, but it
can't push us the other way."

"No," said Dick. "We must push
the wagon with our feet."

So they pushed and pushed.

They pushed it all the way home.

Jane's Dear Old Doll

Jim was playing with his wagon.

"Stop, Jim, stop!" called Jane.

"I want to ride with you.

Baby Doll and Jill want to ride."

Jim stopped and helped Jane put
her dolls into the wagon.

Jane sat behind Jim, and
the dolls sat behind Jane.

"Let's go to the hill," said Jim.

"It is fun to ride down the hill."

Soon they came to the hill.

"Here we go," said Jane.

"Here we go down the hill.

Down the hill!

Down the hill!

Down, down, down!"

Jim pushed, and the wagon

went faster and faster and faster.

"This is fun!" said Jane.

"This is fun!" said Jim.

Bang! Over a bump they went.
How the children were bumped!
How the dolls were bumped!
Out fell the two dolls on the walk.
Over and over they went.
"Ma-ma! Ma-ma!" said Baby Doll.
"Ma-ma! Ma-ma! Ma-ma!"

Soon the wagon was down the hill.
When it stopped, Jane said,
"Oh! Baby Doll and Jill fell out.
We must hurry back and find them."

Jim and Jane began to walk
up the hill. Then they saw a girl.
She was coming down the hill.
"I found two dolls!" she called.
"I am so glad I found them.
I did not have any dolls at all."

"Oh, my!" thought Jane.
"This little girl has found
my two dolls.
I could give her one of them.
I have so many dolls."

Jane looked at her two dolls.
"Let me see," she thought.
"Which one can I give away?
Baby Doll is one of my new dolls.
But Jill is my dear old doll, and
I just can't give her away."

Then Jane said to the little girl,
"The dolls fell out of our wagon.
But you may have one of them.
You may have Baby Doll."

How glad the little girl was!
Jane was glad, too.
She had her dear old Jill again.

Round and Round

"Look!" called Dick.
"See the old black umbrella.
It is a funny merry-go-round.
Who will ride on it?
Who will go round on it?"

"Don't ask me," said Tom.
"Don't ask me or Billy or Peter
or Ellen or Jane or Sally.
We are all too big to ride
on that merry-go-round."

"May Jill ride?" asked Jane.

"May Jill and the other dolls ride?
They are not too big to ride.
Please stop your merry-go-round
and let them ride."

"May Tim ride?" asked Sally.

"Tim is not too big to ride.
Please let him ride."

So Dick stopped his merry-go-round.
He put Tim and the dolls in it.
Then he made it go round again.
Spot and Happy ran round and
round with the merry-go-round.

"Bow-wow, bow-wow," they said.
And all at once they jumped
into the big umbrella.
Jump! Jump!

Bump! Bump! Bump!

Out fell Jill and the other dolls.

Out fell Tim and Spot and Happy.

"Bow-wow! Bow-wow!"
said the two funny dogs.

"Ma-ma! Ma-ma! Ma-ma!"
said the three baby dolls.

"Oh, my!" said Dick. "No one
can ride on this merry-go-round.

It is not any fun at all.

It is just an old umbrella again."

The Wind and the Toys

Sally was playing in the yard.

She had Jill and Tim in her car.

She had her toy dog and toy cat.

Round and round the yard they went.

Soon Mother came to the door.

"Don't you see the rain coming?"
she asked.

"Hurry, Sally, hurry!"

Just then the rain came down.

Sally ran into the house. But she did not take her toys or her car.

Faster and faster fell the rain.

Oo-oo went the wind. Oo-oo!

The wind began to push Sally's car.

It pushed and pushed.

It pushed the car out of the yard and into the street.

Sally's car went along the street.

Then it began to go down the hill.

Down, down the hill it went.

When the rain stopped, Sally went outdoors again.

She looked everywhere for her car.

She looked everywhere for her toys.

"Where is my car?" she asked.

"Where are Toy Dog and Toy Cat?

And where are Tim and Jill?

I wish I had put them in the house when Mother called me."

Just then Sally saw Jack coming along the walk.

He had her car and the toys.

Jack said, "Here is your green car.
The wind pushed it down the hill.
I found it in my yard."
"Thank you, Jack," said Sally.
"I am glad you found my things.
I am glad to have them again."

Sally took the toys to Mother.
"Can you help me?" she asked.
"Look at Jill and my toy animals.
They were outdoors in the rain.
Can you do something for them?"
Mother took Sally's toys and
Jane's dear old Jill.
Soon they were as good as new.

The Birthday Party

"Happy birthday to you, Nancy," said Tom and Susan.

"We have a baby doll for you. It can say ma-ma, ma-ma."

Dick said, "Happy birthday, Nancy. I have a story book for you."

"Oh, thank you!" said Nancy.

"I am glad to get another doll and another story book."

Jane said, "Happy birthday, Nancy.
Here are some paints for you.
Let's open them now."
She helped Nancy open the paints.
"What fine paints!" said Nancy.
"So many pretty colors!
Thank you, Jane, thank you."

Then along came little Sally.
She said, "I have something, too.
Something for the party.
It is a fine red wagon.
Nancy may play with it."

Soon all the children were playing.

But little Sally was not playing
with the other children.

She was playing with the wagon.

She went running round and round
with the fine red wagon.

She pushed it from room to room.

And when the children went to eat,
Sally's fine wagon went along, too.

At last the party was over, and
it was time to go home.

"Good-by, Nancy," said Dick.

"Good-by," said Jane. "We had
a fine time at your party."

"Good-by," said the other children.
"It was a very fine party."

Then Nancy said, "Come again.
And thank you again
for so many pretty things."

All the children went away, and
Sally's fine red wagon went along
with them.

But all at once Dick looked
behind him and saw Sally's wagon.

"Look, Jane!" he said.

"See what Sally has!"

"Oh, Sally!" said Jane.

"That is not your wagon.

It is for Nancy.

It is for her birthday.

You must take it back to Nancy."

"Oh, my!" said Sally.

"I thought it was for me."

She went running back to Nancy.

"Here, Nancy," she said.

"You may have the red wagon.

But you must let me play with it

when I come to see you again."

Story Book Friends

What Was It?

Little Bunny White Tail
was going home for dinner.

Hop, hop he went up the hill.

All at once he saw something
coming down the hill.

It was red, and it was round.

It was going over and over.

A puppy was running after it.

"Well," thought Bunny White Tail.

"What is Fat Puppy running after?

Maybe it is an apple.

I will run and see what it is."

Sleepy Old Cat saw Fat Puppy
running down the hill.

She saw Bunny White Tail
running behind Fat Puppy.

"Mew, mew," said Sleepy Old Cat.

"They are running after something.

It looked like a red bird.

I saw it fly down the hill.

I think I will run after it.

I will get there first and eat it.

It will make a fine dinner."

And away ran Sleepy Old Cat.

Mrs. Duck was on the hill looking
for something to eat.

She saw the animals running.

"Quack! Quack!" said Mrs. Duck.

"What are they running after?

It is something red.

Maybe it is something good to eat.

I don't know what it is.

But I will hurry and get it."

And poky Mrs. Duck did hurry.

Away they all went down the hill.

Poky Mrs. Duck, Sleepy Old Cat,
Bunny White Tail, and Fat Puppy.

Soon they were all down the hill.

They were all looking at Fat Puppy.

They saw a red ball under his feet.

"Oh!" said Bunny White Tail.

"That is not an apple.

Why did I hop after that?"

"Mew!" said Sleepy Old Cat.

"That is not a bird.

Why did I run after that?"

"Quack!" said poky Mrs. Duck.

"That is nothing to eat.

Why did I hurry after that?"

So they all went back up the hill.

Little Duck Talks

One fine day a little yellow duck
went for a walk.

As he walked along the road,
he met Gray Kitten.

"Mew, mew," said Gray Kitten.
And Little Duck thought, "Oh, oh.
What a pretty way to talk!
Why can't I talk that way?"
But he could not say mew, mew.
All he could say was m - ack.
And that was not a pretty way
for a little duck to talk.

Soon Little Duck met Brown Hen
coming along the road.

"Cluck, cluck," said Brown Hen.

And Little Duck thought, "Oh, oh.
What a pretty way to talk!
Why can't I talk that way?
I want to talk like a hen."

But he could not say cluck, cluck.

All he could say was cl - ack.

And that was not a pretty way
for a little duck to talk.

Next Little Duck met a baby robin.

"Peep, peep, peep," said the robin.

And Little Duck thought, "Oh, oh.

What a pretty way to talk!

Why can't I talk that way?

I want to talk like a robin."

But he could not say peep, peep.

All he could say was p - ack.

And that was not a pretty way

for a little duck to talk.

Little Duck was not happy.

He could not say mew, mew.

He could not say cluck, cluck.

He could not say peep, peep.

Then he met old Mrs. Duck
coming along the road.

"Quack, quack," said Mrs. Duck.

"Oh, oh," thought Little Duck.

"That is a very pretty way to talk.

Why can't I talk that way?"

And Little Duck found that he
could say quack, quack very well.

He said it again and again.

He said it all the way home!

Dinner at the Farm

One fine day a pig was running down the road.

He was looking for his dinner.

Soon he saw some corn.

"Wee, wee," said the pig.

"I think that corn will make a fine dinner.

I think it will make me fat."

So the pig ran to the corn and began eating it.

He ate and ate and ate.

A rooster and a brown hen and
her chickens came along.

They saw the pig eating corn.

"Cluck, cluck," said Brown Hen.

"Good morning, dear Mr. Pig.
My chickens and I want our dinner.
Mr. Rooster wants his dinner, too."

"Wee, wee," said Mr. Pig.

"Come in with your chickens.
You can eat corn and get fat."

So Mr. Rooster and Mrs. Brown Hen
and her chickens went in.

They began eating the good corn.

An old white horse came galloping
along the road.

Mrs. Cow came along, too.

"Moo, moo, moo," said Mrs. Cow.

"Good morning to you."

Then she asked, "May we come in?"

"Why not?" asked Mr. Rooster.

And he went on eating.

"Peep, peep," said the chickens.

"Cluck, cluck," said Mrs. Hen.

"Wee, wee, wee," said Mr. Pig.

"Come in, Mrs. Cow, and get fat."

So the cow and the horse went in.

Soon a man came along and saw
the animals eating his corn.

"Get out! Get out!" he called.

"Stop eating my corn!"

Away they all ran down the road.

"Moo, moo," said Mrs. Cow.

"Cluck, cluck," said Brown Hen.

"Peep, peep," said the chickens.

"Wee, wee," said Mr. Pig.

"Good-by, Mr. Man, good-by."

"Good-by," called Mr. Rooster.

"We have had a very good time
eating your corn."

Dark Pony

Every night a little dark pony came running along the road.

Every night he took boys and girls to Sleepy Town.

Every night his four little feet came galloping, galloping, galloping.

His color was dark, and he came at dark.

So that is why all the children called him Dark Pony.

One night a boy met Dark Pony
running along the road.
The little boy called,

"Please take me down
To Sleepy Town."

Dark Pony stopped running.
Up jumped the little boy, and
away they went.
Galloping, galloping, galloping.

173

Soon they met a little girl.
The little girl called,

"Please take me down
To Sleepy Town."

Dark Pony stopped running.
"Jump up," said the boy.
"Jump up behind me."
Up jumped the little girl.
"Go, go, Dark Pony!" she said.
And away they went.
Galloping, galloping, galloping.

174

Next they met a little puppy
running along the road.
The little puppy called,

"Bow-wow, bow-wow,
Please take me now."

Dark Pony stopped, and the puppy
jumped up behind the girl.
"Go, go, Dark Pony," they said.
And away they went galloping,
galloping, galloping.

Then they met Gray Squirrel.
Gray Squirrel called,

"Please take me, too.
Take me with you."

"Jump up," said the puppy.
"Jump up behind me."
So the little gray squirrel
jumped up behind the puppy.
"Go, go, Dark Pony!" they said.
And away they went galloping,
galloping, galloping, galloping.
On the road to Sleepy Town.

How happy they all were!

They sang and sang and sang.

Soon Dark Pony began to go slower
and slower and slower and slower.

He was coming to Sleepy Town.

The puppy, the squirrel, the boy,
and the girl were all very sleepy.

And so was Dark Pony.

Slower and slower he went,
and at last he stopped.

He had come to Sleepy Town.

And so had the puppy, the squirrel,
the boy, and the girl.

They all had come to Sleepy Town.

The Big Brown Basket

One morning a little old woman
went down the road.

She had a big brown basket.

She was very happy.

So she sang and sang and sang,

"I must go down,
   Down to the town,
   Down to the town
   With my basket."

The woman soon met a fat pig.

"Wee, wee," said the pig.

Then he asked,

"What is in your brown basket?"

"Nothing for you," said the woman.

"May I see?" asked the pig.

"I will give you some pennies."

The little old woman said, "Yes.

Come along with me to the town.

Then I will open the basket.

Then you may look, Mr. Pig.

Then you may look in my basket."

Then they met a white rooster.

"Please open your basket," he said.

"May I see what you have
in your basket?"

"Nothing for you," said the woman.

"May I see?" asked the rooster.

"I will give you some pennies."

The little old woman said, "Yes.
Come along with me to the town.
Then I will open the basket.
Then you may look, Mr. Rooster."
So they went down the road.

The rooster, the funny fat pig, and
the little old woman.

Next they met Mrs. Cow.

"Moo, moo," said the cow.

"I wish I could see in that basket.

I can not guess what is in it."

"Nothing for you," said the woman.

"May I see?" asked the cow.

"I will give you some pennies."

The little old woman said, "Yes.

Come along with me to the town.

Then I will open my basket.

Then you may look, Mrs. Cow."

So they went down the road.

The funny fat pig, the rooster,

the cow, and the little old woman.

At last they came to the town.
"Now," said the little old woman.
"Now give me all of your pennies.
Then I will open my basket.
Then you may see what is in it."

Soon the brown basket was open,
and all the animals looked.
"Moo, moo," said the cow.
"There is nothing at all
in the basket."
"Nothing at all!" said the pig.
"Nothing at all!" said the rooster.
"Nothing at all in the basket."

The little old woman said, "Come!
We will put something good
in the basket."
So they went to a store in the town
and put something good in the basket.
"Now," said the little old woman.
"Now there is food in the basket."

"Moo, moo," said the cow.
"Now we are glad.
We are glad there is food
in the basket."

The woman sat under a tree.

"Now come to my party," she said.

So they all began eating the food.

Eating and eating and eating!

Soon there was nothing at all,

nothing at all in the basket.

How happy they were!

They sang, and they sang, and

they sang.

And at last they all went home.

The funny fat pig, the rooster,

the cow, and the little old woman.

The Merry-Go-Round

Once a merry-go-round came to town.

And a fine merry-go-round it was.

It had horses of every color.

Round and round it went.

It sang and sang and sang.

All the children came running.

"Let's ride. Let's ride," they called.

"Let's ride on the merry-go-round."

So all the children jumped on.

Round and round they went.

Round and round went the horses.

Galloping, galloping, galloping!

The children said, "Go faster!
Go faster, Merry-go-round."
"I will go," said the merry-go-round.
"I will go faster and faster.
I will not stop at all."
Round and round went the horses.
Faster and faster and faster!
The children sang and sang,

"This is the way
   We like to play,
   Galloping, galloping
   All the day."

Round and round they went.

At last the fathers and mothers
came to the merry-go-round.

They wanted the children
to go home.

The fathers and mothers called,
"Stop, stop, Merry-go-round!

Why don't you stop?

Night is coming, and our children
must go home.

Please stop, Merry-go-round."

The merry-go-round did not want
to stop. It sang and sang,

"Go away. Go away!
I will run all day."

The horses did not stop, and so
the children did not stop.

Then the merry-go-round said,
"I will go faster and faster."

But the merry-go-round
could not go faster and faster.

It began to go slower and slower.

The horses went slower, and
the children went slower.

Slower and slower and slower!

At last they all stopped.

"Oh, my!" said the merry-go-round.

"I have run down."

Then the children jumped down
from the horses.

Some of the children fell.

Some of them could not walk.

So the mothers and fathers
helped them.

Some feet went this way, and
some feet went that way.

They went this way
            and that way
      and this way
            and that way
      all the way home.

TO THE TEACHER

Our New Friends follows *Fun with Dick and Jane,* the primer of the BASIC READERS in the CURRICULUM FOUNDATION SERIES. All words in *Fun with Dick and Jane* are repeated early and adequately in this book. Likewise, all the different words in this book are carried over and maintained in *Friends and Neighbors,* the basic reader for early second grade, which immediately follows *Our New Friends.*

The *Think-and-Do Book* to accompany *Our New Friends* provides further development of word meanings and practice in recognition.

VOCABULARY LIST

The following list contains the 178 words introduced in *Our New Friends.* All inflectional variants of a word, with the exception of the plural *s*-forms of nouns and the singular *s*-forms of verbs, are counted as new words. Combinations of letters representing sounds that are not words are not counted.

UNIT I			
5 —	22 first	38 man	56 once
6 lives	23 going	which	were
7 maybe	24 name	39 Bill	57 has
8 day	your	40 —	58 color
9 —	25 —	41 found	paint
10 —	26 —	42 five	59 —
11 Peter	27 know	store	60 painted
Ellen	take	43 —	swish
12 wagon	28 —	44 —	61 made
let	29 street	45 —	very
13 —	them	46 —	62 head
14 —	30 Jim		feet
15 put	Patty	UNIT II	63 next
her	31 then	47 —	him
16 us	lost	48 hurry	64 give
walk	32 pennies	49 things	Billy
17 rain	buy	50 dinner	65 worked
umbrella	33 —	51 basket	66 don't
18 splash	34 pocket	52 old	67 making
19 —	35 —	53 busy	68 Bird
20 —	36 walked	after	69 —
21 time	37 last	54 back	70 can't
	way	55 his	71 poky

190

72 outdoors
   as
73 bang
74 stop
75 green
   tree
76 —
77 reads
   sleep
78 book
   story
79 began
   laugh
80 slower

UNIT III

81 —
82 when
   some
83 could
   wish
84 ask
85 coming
   be
86 Nancy
87 let's
   think
88 milk
   called
89 from
90 —
91 of
92 room
   had
93 door
94 jumped
   bumped
95 —
96 yard
97 feed
   night

98 every
99 dear
100 everywhere
    morning
101 Bunny
    open
102 surprise
    fell
103 helped
    thought
104 just
    another
105 how
106 Dick's
107 took
    nuts
108 gray
    squirrel
109 —
110 any
111 snow
    food
112 party
113 corn
    apples
114 —
115 behind
116 —
117 valentine
118 an
119 nest
120 —
121 robins
122 fly
123 —
124 —
125 —
126 —

UNIT IV

127 —

128 Jane's
    over
129 glad
    again
130 looking
    playing
131 Sally's
132 —
133 many
134 other
135 or
    nothing
136 —
137 —
138 —
139 wind
    push
140 faster
    stopped
141 pushed
142 Jill
    hill
143 —
144 —
145 —
146 may
147 round
    merry-go-
    round
148 asked
149 —
150 —
151 along
152 —
153 —
154 —
155 fine
156 running
157 —
158 —

UNIT V

159 —
160 puppy
    Fat
161 Sleepy
162 Mrs.
163 why
164 road
    met
165 Brown
166 peep
167 —
168 wee
    eating
169 rooster
    Mr.
170 galloping
    moo
171 —
172 Dark
    Town
173 —
174 —
175 —
176 —
177 sang
178 woman
179 —
180 —
181 —
182 —
183 —
184 —
185 —
186 —
187 —
188 —
189 —

191

ACKNOWLEDGMENTS

For permission to adapt and use copyrighted material, grateful acknowledgment is made to Dorothy Baruch for "Who Will Ride?" from "The Express Wagon" in *The Two Bobbies*, published by The John Day Company; to Harper & Brothers for "Fun in the New House" from "The Rainy-Day Story" in *The Stories of Peter and Ellen* by Gertrude Smith; to the authors, *Storytime*, and The Baptist Sunday School Board for "The Big Umbrella" from "The Good Partner" by Alice Whitson Norton and for "Poky Gets Lost" from "The Traveling Turtle" by Esther Miller Payler; to the authors and *Children's Activities* for "A Big Friend" from "Binky and Babs and Mr. Bones" by Curtis Haseltine, for "Puff Has a Ride" from "Where Was Sparky?" by Ednah A. Parr, and for "The Lost Toys" from "Kenny-Boy and the Lost Ball" by Rowena Bennett; to David C. Cook Publishing Company and *Dew Drops* for "Who Will Help Tom?" from "Freddie Wanted Help" by Eleanor Lockwood; to Miriam Clark Potter for "Patty and Her Pennies" from "Constance Had a Penny"; to Alice Dalgliesh for "Old Toy Horse" from "The Story of Dobbin" in *Junior Home Magazine*; to Ethel Calvert Phillips for "The Little House" from "A Present for Three" and to Maud Lindsay for "Making Boats" from "Three Little Boats," both in *American Childhood*; to *The Youth's Companion* (now combined with *The American Boy*) for "Happy Finds a Friend" from "What Happened to Happy" by Nancy Byrd Turner, for "Red Hen and the Valentine" from "Biddy Brown's Egg" by Eleanor F. Pease, for "The Big Brown Basket" from "The Old Woman and Her Very Big Basket" by Elsie Parrish, for "The Snow Party" from "The Winter Picnic" by James Deehan, for "Who Took the Nuts?" from "Pockets" by Edna P. Brett, and for "Jane's Dear Old Doll" from "The Best Doll" by Jessie Lathrop; to the authors and *Child Life* for "What Was It?" from "Drop It, Brownie" by Charlotte Wolff and for "Little Duck Talks" from "Little Duckling Tries His Voice" by Marjorie M. La Fleur; to J. L. Hammett Company for "A Home in a Tree" from "What Was in the Nest?" in *Boston Collection of Kindergarten Stories*; to James Tippett for "The Wind and the Umbrella" from "The Blue Umbrella" in *Told Under the Blue Umbrella*; to Junior Home Magazine, Inc., publishers of *Junior Home Magazine*, for "The Wind and the Toys" from "Left Out in the Rain" by Maizie Barney; to Milton Bradley Company for "Dinner at the Farm" from "The Little Pig" in *More Mother Stories* by Maud Lindsay; to Thomas Nelson & Sons for "Bunny Boy" from "How Bunnyboy Was Named" in *Playmates in Print* by Edna Whiteman; to *Little Folks Magazine* for "Dark Pony"; to Rowena Bennett for "Sally Helps" from "Tommy Tells about Going to Grandmother's Farm," for "Playing Store" from the story of the same name, and for "Round and Round" from "The Merry-Go-Round."

"The Merry-Go-Round" is taken by permission from Caroline Emerson's *The Merry-Go-Round of Modern Tales*, published and copyrighted by E. P. Dutton & Company, Inc., New York.